The
Model Engineer
Series
No. 8

Price 6D. Net

Simple Electrical Working Models

HOW TO MAKE AND USE THEM

FULLY ILLUSTRATED

FOURTH EDITION

Model
Electric Beam
Engine

Contains full instructions for making a Model Electric Telegraph, an Electric Bell, a Simple Telephone, a Portable Shocking Coil, several forms of Small Electric Motors, and a Model Electric Beam Engine.

PERCIVAL MARSHALL & CO., LONDON, E.C.

Simple Electrical Working Models

Originally published by
Percival Marshall & Co.
London

Reprinted by
Lindsay Publications Inc
Bradley IL 60915

ISBN 1-55918-259-8

1 2 3 4 5 6 7 8 9 0

2001

WARNING

The "*Model Engineer*" Series. No. 8

SIMPLE ELECTRICAL
WORKING MODELS

HOW TO MAKE AND USE THEM

*A Practical Handbook for Electrical Amateurs
and Students*

FULLY ILLUSTRATED

EDITED BY

PERCIVAL MARSHALL, A.I.MECH.E.

FOURTH EDITION

LONDON
PERCIVAL MARSHALL & CO.
26-29 POPPIN'S COURT, FLEET STREET, E.C.

CONTENTS

PREFACE

THE amateur or student who turns his attention to the fascinating possibilities of electrical science is usually possessed of a keen desire to give practical effect to his knowledge by constructing "something that will work." He will find in the pages of this little book a number of exercises for his skill, each of which will serve to illustrate in miniature one or other of the numerous present-day industrial applications of the electric current. None of the models or appliances described require a very high degree of constructional ability, nor the possession of a very elaborate outfit of tools, so that they should all be within the power of the merest tyro to make. At the same time, they will all give very satisfactory results if the instructions given are faithfully carried out, and will well repay the trouble of making by reason of the instruction and enjoyment they will afford.

It should be mentioned that these descriptions and illustrations are the work of various contributors to *The Model Engineer*, in the pages of which journal the matter first appeared. Instructions for making suitable batteries for working the models herein described will be found in No. 5 of " The Model Engineer " series of handbooks.

PERCIVAL MARSHALL.

LONDON, E.C.

SIMPLE ELECTRICAL WORKING MODELS

———◆———

CHAPTER I

How to Make a Model Electric Telegraph

It seems a fitting commencement to this series to start with a model electric telegraph—one of the first, as it was also one of the most important, applications of the electric force. The instrument described in this chapter is of a type still very largely used, and differing from its prototype principally in point of strength and size. Attention may first be drawn to the general perspective view of the instrument to be described. It is shown in fig. 1; and the next point is a consideration of the materials required for its construction. These consist principally of some cigar-box wood, thin springy brass, brass and copper wire, and for the necessary battery a small piece each of sheet copper and zinc. Two pieces of wood (any kind will do), about 4 ins. long, 3 ins. wide, and $\frac{3}{8}$ in. thick, will

be needed for the baseboards—for here it may be
stated that the following remarks include the
making of *two* instruments.   This is necessary
when two operators are to work, although one can
very well practise on one instrument, so that if
practice only is desired, one instrument will be
sufficient.

The baseboards, B B (fig. 2), must be nice and

The Complete Instrument

FIG. 1.—Model Electric Telegraph.

square.   Possibly two ends of a wooden box can
be found somewhat about the size given, and a
vigorous application of sandpaper will make the
top smooth.   The edges may be chamfered (as at
c, fig. 2) if you have a plane or even a chisel, or
merely rounded neatly with the sandpaper.   It
may be stained or varnished, or both, according to

taste; and if this is done now, a better job will

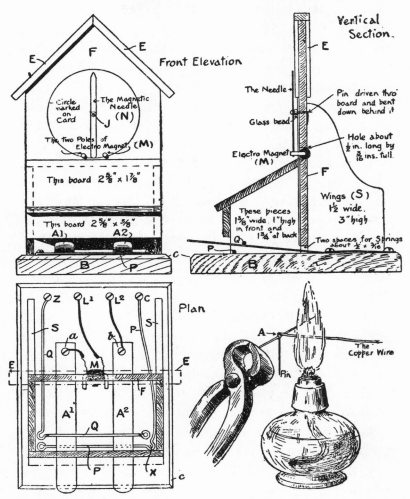

FIG. 2.—A Simple Model Telegraph Instrument.

FIG. 4.—Soldering the Needle
to the Pivot Pin.

result than if it is left till the parts are fitted
together.

Now cut from the cigar-box wood two pieces to form the upright board, F, for each instrument. These will be $2\frac{3}{4}$ ins. wide, $4\frac{1}{4}$ ins. high in the middle, and 3 ins. at the sides. They can be cut with the penknife or fretsaw, and should have all the edges nice and straight; indeed, the more care spent on getting edges straight and corners square, the better will the finished instrument appear. Then cut four pieces the shape of S, these being to form wings or supports for the upright boards. Their dimensions are not very important, and can be taken from the sectional drawing (fig. 2). The same remarks apply to the pieces of wood forming the box in the front of the instrument, the principal point to be observed being neatness. The front of this box does not reach down to the baseboard, being stopped short about $\frac{3}{8}$ in. above, as shown, to let the contact springs, A1 and A2, through. Next cut four little strips, $2\frac{1}{4}$ ins. long, $\frac{1}{4}$ in. wide, from the cigar box to form the edging, E E, on top of the board, F. These strips must be cut with a mitred joint at the top to get the best effect. It can be done with the penknife. None of the pieces already cut out will be fitted together just yet, except temporarily, as there will still be work to do upon them.

Attention must now be turned to the magnetic needle, N. There is here scope for some little ingenuity, as it may be made in a variety of ways. The best material is a length of watch-spring about $\frac{1}{16}$ in. or $\frac{3}{32}$ in. wide; but a piece of steel wire, fine knitting-needle, an ordinary needle, or even a narrow strip of thin steel like a broken fret-saw blade, may be pressed into service. Whatever the form, the material *must* be steel. We will suppose, first, that the watch-spring is available. Having cut a piece 1½ ins. long, it must be softened by heating to redness in a spirit lamp flame, Bunsen burner, or fire, and allowed to cool slowly. Perhaps the simplest way will be to place the strip length-wise on the end of a poker and bind it down tightly with some iron wire, entirely covering the needle, as may be seen in the little sketch (fig. 3). If this be next inserted in the clear part of a fire, and left till the poker, wire, and steel strip are all a good bright red, they may then be withdrawn and the poker end pushed amongst the ashes under the fire and left to cool down slowly. If two instru-ments are being made, it is quite as easy to do the two strips as one at the same operation.

The needle—which the strip of steel may now be called—on being unbound, will, of course, be blackened, and the first process will be to polish it. This is easily accomplished with the aid of some fine emery cloth, care being taken to avoid buckling the needle. Next measure the total length of the strip, halve the amount, and make a mark $\frac{1}{32}$ in. on one side of the middle, thus :—

A tiny hole must be made at the mark. If you

have an Archimedean drill, put in the finest bit and drill until the point of the drill only is just going through to the other side of the strip. In drilling little pieces of metal like this, a couple of pins driven in the bench, one on each side of the work (as at *a* and *b* in the sketch above), will save trouble by preventing the work from running round with the drill. As soon as the point of drill appears on the other side, turn the needle over and give one or two turns to the drill from the second side, so as to make a clean small hole, which should be just large enough to run quite freely on a small pin—one of the common domestic pins, about $\frac{5}{8}$ in. long, being most suitable. The needle may be shaped off with a small file at its two ends (as at N in fig. 2), and this will give a neat finish. Straighten the needle, if necessary, before the next operation.

If the reader does not possess a drill of any sort, he may punch a tiny hole by cutting off an inch or so from an ordinary knitting-needle, and carefully filing one end of the short length on four sides, thus :—

This must be used to punch the hole in the strip, first from one side and then from the other, light blows being only used. When a small opening has been made, the little burr on one side of the strip may be filed off, when the hole will probably be found big enough to run on a small pin freely. The hole having been made, it will then be necessary to harden the needle. This is done by heating it to a bright red heat in a spirit lamp or Bunsen flame. Have ready a cup of cold water right alongside the flame, and the moment the needle is red hot from one end to the other, pop it as quickly as possible into the water. The needle should be held by a piece of thin wire wrapped once or twice round the middle. The quicker the transference from the flame to the water, the harder and better will it be.

If a watch-spring is not available, a very good magnetic needle can be made from an ordinary sewing-needle, and this can be so manipulated as not to need the softening and hardening processes. On the other hand, it is not so readily seen as the watch-spring needle, and not so 'professional' looking. Obtain a fairly stout needle about $1\frac{3}{4}$ ins. long; if longer, the 'eye' may be broken off, and also a portion of the point end. Now take a thin pin, cut off the head, and, with a few light blows with a hammer, beat out the thick portion flat for about $\frac{1}{8}$ in. By means of the pincers and hammer, bend this round the needle not quite at the middle, and make it clasp the needle as tight as possible. The writer finds it best to solder the two together, and to do this without softening (and thereby spoiling) the needle is worth describing. The method is shown in the sketch (page 9, fig. 4). First scrape a few grains of solder from a stick of the same (or from a soldered seam in any tin can), and powder up a tiny heap of resin.   Take a piece of copper or brass wire about $\frac{1}{32}$ in. thick and 6 ins. long; clean one end, heat that end in the spirit lamp flame, and immediately dip it among the resin and solder scrapings. If done quickly, the end of the wire will be ' tinned,' taking up some of the solder which will coat the wire beautifully.   Now take a pinch of the powdered resin and work it with the fingers well into the joint where the pin has been wrapped round the needle (see A in the sketch, fig. 4).   Warm the copper wire again, not letting it get too hot; and having dipped it in the resin, take up one or two solder filings on the end.   By means of pincers or pliers, hold the needle in the left hand, keeping it horizontal and the pin downwards.   Bring it near the spirit lamp flame, but not near enough to allow the heat of the latter to affect the needle (which would at once be shown by the latter turning suddenly a blue colour).   If now the wire end, with the solder attached, be placed on A, just as sketched, the heat from the flame will travel along and very soon melt the particles of solder.   These will at once adhere to the pin, but the wire must be worked about until the needle also gets a coating.   A very little will do, and perseverance is bound to be followed by success.   Hold the needle by the pincers till cold, when the joint may be cleaned by very gently scraping with the point of a penknife.   It must be noted that in the sketch the further end of the needle is *beyond*, not *in*, the flame of the lamp.

The next process is that of magnetising the needle.

If the reader possesses an ordinary horseshoe permanent magnet, this is a simple matter. Lay the needle across the two poles of the magnet and rub it backwards and forwards (as at fig. 5) two or three dozen times, when it will be ready. Perhaps a magnet of this kind is not amongst the amateur's possessions, but he possibly has access to an electric bell and battery. This can very well be used for

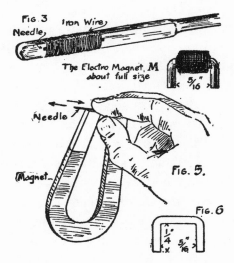

Fig. 3 Iron Wire,
Needle,

The Electro Magnet, M
about full size

5/16"

Needle

Magnet

Fig. 5.

Fig. 6

1/4"
5/16"
x

the purpose, the writer finding it easy to make a needle sufficiently magnetic to carry quite three times its own weight by this method.

To use the electric bell magnet properly, the armature of the bell must be removed by taking out the two screws which secure its contact spring to the bell frame. A short piece of wire must be used so as to allow the current to pass through the magnet winding, when it will be found that the poles show strong magnetisation. Place the needle across these poles, where it will stick fast, and give it a number of sharp taps with, say, a penknife, leaving it in position for a couple of minutes. No further treatment is necessary, but do not forget to replace the bell armature and make the connections good.

It is now required to make the little electro-magnet, M; this is pretty clearly shown, full size. The simplest way to make it is as follows :—First take an ordinary French nail 1 in. long; this should be about $\frac{1}{16}$ in. diameter. Cut off the head and point, leaving it still about $\frac{7}{8}$ in. long, and soften it in the fire. It is not necessary, however, to spend much time in allowing it to cool, as the iron from which the nail is made is already of a comparatively soft nature. Now make two marks on the nail with a file, making the central portion $\frac{5}{16}$ in. long, and the two end portions equal to each other. Hold the nail in the vice, or in a pair of strong pincers, just at one of the marks, and bend over at right angles with a few blows of the hammer. Treat the other end likewise, taking care that both the bent ends lie in the same plane, and when a little adjusting has been done to make all square and ship-shape, you should have a little soft iron magnet core very much of the shape and dimensions shown at fig. 6. This has to be wound with the fine wire to make it an electro-magnet. About 1 yard of No. 36 or 38 silk-covered or single cotton-covered copper wire will be sufficient for each electro-magnet (one being needed for each instrument), so that a pennyworth should be ample. Be most careful not to kink or break this fine wire, nor to tear off the insulation at any place. Three layers of wire must be wound quite evenly on the central portion of the magnet, fastening the end of the wire by drawing it fairly tightly under the very last turn. The magnet should now be about $\frac{3}{16}$ in. diameter over the wire. Having done both magnets, put them aside until they can be tested.

A diversion may here be made in order to describe the battery which will be necessary to use with the telegraph. The excuse for thus running ahead lies in the fact that it is better to test the little electro-magnets before going any further with the instrument. Unfortunately, not even the cheapest battery can be made from materials likely to be in possession of an amateur just ' beginning.' Still, a very simple battery can be made which will cost very little. This battery, the elements of which are shown in fig. 7, has strips of zinc and copper immersed in plain vinegar. Obtain some scraps of zinc from a plumber or builder: scraps from which four pieces, about 2 ins. long by $1\frac{1}{2}$ ins. wide, can be cut are suitable. The thickness is immaterial. The copper will probably have to be purchased: enough to provide four pieces, $4\frac{1}{2}$ ins. by $1\frac{1}{2}$ ins., will be required. Very thin stuff will do, and its real value would not be more than 2d. Now cut from what will be the top of the zinc the two corners, as shown

B

in fig. 7. Then cut slips of wood from the cigar box, long enough to stretch across a cup (3 ins. or thereabouts), and $\frac{3}{8}$ in. wide. The piece of zinc has to be enclosed between two such slips, the end of a piece of copper wire being inserted between the zinc and the wood so as to get a good bearing on the former. The surfaces of the wire and zinc where they touch must be scraped or rubbed clean with sandpaper or file. The ends

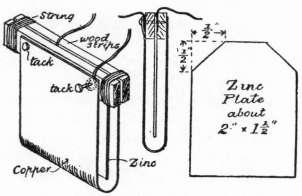

Fig. 7.—Details of the Battery.

of the wood strips beyond the zinc should then be tied tightly together with thin string; this will hold the zinc securely. It is shown in fig. 7. A copper strip is now taken, and one short end laid on the outside of one of the wood strips, and a small tack driven through the corner of the copper and both pieces of wood.

Observe that the tack *makes no contact with the zinc*, it is for this purpose that the corners of the zinc sheet were cut off. Treat the other corner of the copper in the same way. Now double the copper strip so that the other end of it comes on the outside of the other wood strip, and make sure that a clear space of about $\frac{1}{8}$ in. exists between the zinc and copper all round. Drive in two more tacks at the corners of the copper on the side just doubled over, still being careful not to come into contact with the zinc. The rule to be remembered is this : That no metallic contact of any sort may exist between the zinc and copper, except through the line wires and external circuit of the battery. Before driving the last tack quite home, make a little loop on the end of a copper wire, and place this loop between the copper and wood, so that when this last nail is driven in, it will go through the loop and hold the copper tightly down on the wire. This will be understood on reference to fig. 7, where the loop is shown dotted at the right-hand corner of the perspective sketch.

If the tacks have been properly driven, the zinc and copper ' couple' should now be ready, being tightly held together with the wood strips and tacks, and wires coming—one from the zinc and the other from the copper plate. Four such ' couples' should be made for two instruments, and to test the electro-magnet, proceed as follows :—

Put two of the copper-zinc pairs into two teacups, and twist together the wires coming from the *zinc* of one, and from the *copper* of the other cell. The end of the fine wire on the little magnet should now be gently cleaned and twisted once or twice round one of the remaining battery wires—either will do. Pour in some vinegar in each cup until nearly full, or nearly up to the wood strips, and then hold the free end of the magnet winding against the one remaining battery wire. The electro-magnet should be strong enough to hold up a good-sized nail placed across its two poles, and should easily attract or repel one end of your magnetised needle when one of its poles is approached within $\frac{1}{4}$ in. of the electro-magnet.

All being satisfactory, the battery may be put aside, and the further construction of the instrument proceeded with. It may, however, be here remarked that diluted sulphuric acid—about 12 to 15 parts water to 1 of acid, by weight—will form a better and more lasting solution to work this little battery.

Some stoutish brass wire is now required, 1 yard of No. 16 or 18 gauge being quite sufficient for the two telegraphs, and this wire should be clean and bright. Be careful not to bend it anywhere but where a bend is intentional, as the clean straight parts make the apparatus look more business-like. Cut off two pieces $5\frac{3}{4}$ ins. long (one piece for each instrument), and with a small pair of pliers make a loop at each end big enough for the shank of a small round-headed brass screw to go through. Then, 2 ins. from one of the loops, make a loop of the fashion of

X (fig. 2), which also shows the complete shape of this piece of wire (P, on fig. 2) and how it must be bent. Two other pieces of wire (shown separately in fig. 8) are not so easily described, as, although they are much the same on plan, the front straight part is made into a long flat arch. I have tried to show this in the perspective sketch in fig. 8, and the form can also be gathered from

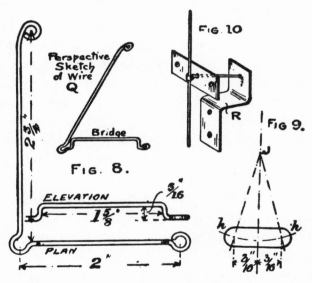

Q (fig. 2). These wires have to be fixed down on the baseboard by means of round-headed brass screws through the various loops, and all the positions are shown in fig. 2.

The brass strips or springs, A1 and A2 (fig. 2), ought to be dealt with now. They should be springy, 3 ins. by $\frac{3}{8}$ in., and fairly thick. Holes must be punched at a and b to screw the springs down.

Holes may be punched in thin metals by filing off the point of a French nail so as to leave a circular flat surface, and using this as a punch. A piece of waste boxwood, oak, beech, or other hard wood, must support the metal, and a good sharp blow given, sufficient to drive the punch right through at one operation. For the present purpose any springy metal will do, even tin plate may be made to serve, but clock-spring, although suitable, would be found no easy job to provide with suitable holes. After the latter have been made, the springs may be screwed down in position, being so bent that when tightly screwed down they both press upwards against the arched wire, Q. By pressing the outer end of either spring, it must 'break' contact with this wire and 'make' contact with the second wire, P, beneath it. Before finally fixing the springs, cut off some short lengths of copper wire of moderate thickness, and making a small loop at one end of each, put the loops over the holes, a and b, and drive in the screws. These wires provide the connections to the springs.

It will now be a good plan to put together the front box part of the apparatus shown in figs. 1 and 2; then put it in position, with the backboard, F, in its place. Where the wires, P and Q, go through, small nicks may be cut in the bottom of F to allow it to bear properly on the baseboard; spaces have also to be cut for the springs to work in—about $\frac{1}{2}$ in. by $\frac{3}{16}$ in. will do. Next mark a point on the centre line of F for the position of the needle centre, as at J. This must be just high enough to allow the bottom of needle to swing clear of front box. Take the board, F, and, with J as centre, draw an arc, $h\,h$ (see fig. 9), the radius of which should be $\frac{1}{16}$ in. less than the longer portion of the needle. On this arc mark off two points from the centre line about $\frac{3}{16}$ in. each way; then at each of the points so found, draw a little circle $\frac{3}{16}$ in. diameter. Join the tops of these two circles and also the bottoms, and cut out the piece thus marked out with a fretsaw or penknife. This is for the electro-magnet, M, which should fit snugly in the space, with the two poles pointing to the front.

The method of fixing the magnetic needle depends on its form. If the watch-spring pattern with drilled hole has been made, a suitable support will be a thin small pin very carefully driven in at J, and bent down at the back of the board, F. If the ordinary needle—mounted as already described—is used, its fixing will not be quite so simple a matter. The best plan will be to cut pieces of thin brass or tin plate, and punch or drill a very tiny hole, just big enough to let the pin run in freely, in the middle. A hole may then be punched at each end, by means of which the plate is tacked to the board, F, in front (by means of short pins), so that the central hole comes at J. A fair-sized hole should be bored in the wood at J. (This arrangement is shown in fig. 10, the board, F, being omitted.) The back bearing (R, in fig. 10) is another piece of thin sheet, with holes punched as for the front plate ; but the plate has to be shaped as shown, so as to take a bearing as far back as possible. The point of the pin has also to be bent down after passing through the bearing, R. Before mounting the needle or magnet, the whole of the front of the board, F, has to be covered by a piece of thin card or stout paper, fastened on by thin glue, which should be allowed to set under the pressure of a few heavy books. Should the hole in needle be drilled too near the middle, it will be found difficult to get it to hang nicely. In that case, one end should be made a little heavier than the other, by melting on to it a small bulb of sealing wax, care being taken not to soften the steel.

The strips, E E (fig. 2), are fixed to the board, F, by means of two or three short pins driven through each, and the same fastening secures F to the front box. These are then glued down together to the baseboard. The magnet, M, is then to be put in its place, two small holes being made in the cardboard to allow the poles to project through at least $\frac{1}{16}$ in. The magnet can be fixed by dropping on to it several drops of hot sealing wax (which must not be burning, however), or by glueing over it a strip of paper on the back. One of its wire ends is then bared, cleaned, and wrapped temporarily round the end of the wire proceeding from the spring, A1. The other end is likewise temporarily connected to a wire which is fixed down by the screw, L1. The wire from spring, A2, is connected to a fourth screw, L2, at the back of the instrument.

The needle, N, may next be fitted. If of the watch-spring variety, thread the needle on a small pin, then thread on a very small glass bead, which must have a hole large enough to give it plenty of play, and finally drive in the pin at J until it just leaves the needle enough freedom to turn easily. It should hang with the lower end between the two

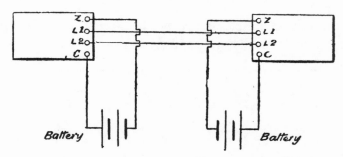

FIG. 11.—Diagram to show how to connect up two Instruments.

poles of the magnet, and an equal space on each side—in fact, as shown in fig. 2.

The instrument is now ready for testing, and, if two have been made, they should be connected up to each other. This is done by hooking an end of a piece of copper wire round the wire near the screw, L1, of one telegraph, and hooking the other end of same wire round the corresponding wire of the second apparatus. Then the ends of another wire are similarly joined up to L2 on each instrument. If these are 'bare' wires, they must not be allowed to touch one another anywhere.

The batteries are next prepared. Two cells are needed for each instrument, these being connected up as already described, and the wire from the free copper end of each battery joined to the wire at C (fig. 2), and that from the zinc end to Z. A diagram is given (fig. 11) to show this, so that no mistake should be made. The vinegar having been poured into all four cells, the first trials may be made. In fig. 11 the batteries are shown in the usual diagrammatic form.

Signalling must, of course, be given in the proper code, and this is here reproduced:—

A√ B∕∖∖ C∧∧ D∕∖∖ E∖ F∖∧˙
G∕∧ H∖∖∖ I∖∖ J√∕∕ K∕∖ L∖∧∖
M∕∕ N∕∧ O∕∕∕ P√∕∖ Q∕∕∖ R√∖
S∖∖∖ T∕ U∖∖∕ V∖∖∖ W√∕ X∕∖∕
Y∕∖∕ Z∕∕∕∖

It will, perhaps, be best to cut this out, or copy it neatly on to a piece of paper the right size, and paste it down on the sloping lid of the instrument as shown in fig. 1. It is then instantly available for reference.

On depressing the left-hand spring, A1, the bottom of needle should at once fly in this direction / on both instruments; and, on depressing A2, the needle ought to assume this position \. If the needle of either instrument does not spring to the correct position, the connections of the electro-magnet of that instrument must be reversed, when all should be right. The same effects should occur whichever telegraph is used, the needles of both working in unison.

Should the needle refuse to move, it points to a bad connection or broken wire—that is, if it has been really properly magnetised—and such fault must be looked for and remedied. If the needle tends to stick to the magnet poles, these should be covered by a tiny piece of gummed paper, so that the needle end touches—not the bare iron, but a paper surface.

All being well, the connections may be properly twisted up, and the wing-pieces of wood, S, glued in position to strengthen the instrument, which is now complete. The careful worker should now have a very presentable model telegraph of quite a practical character, whose cost, all told, may be well under a shilling.

CHAPTER II

How to Make an Electric Bell

WE deal in this chapter with the construction of an electric bell, which is to have a $2\frac{1}{2}$-in. gong. We shall require a piece of $\frac{5}{16}$-in. round iron, bent into a horseshoe, or, rather, letter U shape, and $1\frac{3}{8}$ ins. long in the straight and $\frac{9}{16}$ in. apart inside. This is for the magnet core. Soften the core by placing it in the kitchen fire overnight, and taking it out of the ashes in the morning. By this method the iron is made red hot, and very gradually cooled, thus making the metal as soft as possible. Now clean off the scale, and file up the ends true and square with each other.

We now proceed to make the magnet coils. There are two methods of winding these coils. One is to make a bobbin of stout brown paper, 1 in. long, to fit each magnet limb. The bobbin ends may be either brown paper, cardboard, thin fretwood, vulcanite, or fibre, but they must be firmly fastened to the brown paper tube. The ends should be 1 in. diameter.

The other way is to make a paper tube, and then wind the first layer of wire the length required— 1 in. The next layer is left one turn short, and

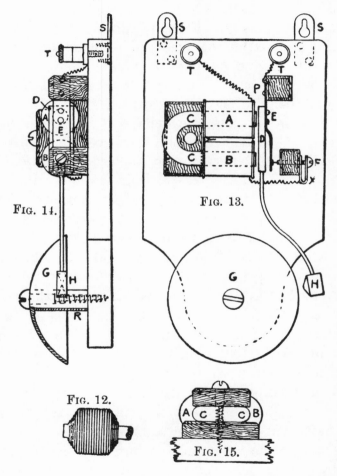

FIG. 14.

FIG. 13.

FIG. 12.

FIG. 15.

the layer above, another turn short at each end, as in fig. 12. This method saves the trouble of bobbin ends, but is much more difficult to carry out, as, if due care is not taken, the wire falls away at the ends of the coil. It is possible to get over this difficulty, however, if the method described in Chapter VI., page 49, on the construction of a Permanent Magnet Electro - Motor, be adopted. Having decided on our method of winding, we rig up a little windlass with a spindle to fit in our bobbins. We shall require a 4-oz. reel of No. 22 green, either silk or cotton covered wire. If white covered wire is used, the coils will require a coat or two of shellac varnish when wound. This is made by dissolving orange shellac in methylated spirit. Two coats of rather thin varnish will give a much better finish than one coat of thick. The 4-oz. reel will be ample for our purpose. Leave about 6 ins. of wire before commencing to wind, and wind each coil full, that is, to about 1 in. outside diameter, with about 6 ins. to spare at the finishing end. Wind each coil in exactly the same way and direction. Now slip the coils on the magnet limbs so that the iron projects a good $\frac{1}{16}$ in. beyond the coil ends, and with both starting ends toward the bend. Make a short coil of each starting end by winding the wire round a piece of $\frac{1}{8}$-in. wire, clean the ends for about 1 in. up, twist, and solder them together.

The baseboard next claims our attention. It is made from a piece of mahogany, walnut, or even deal will do if anything else cannot be had. A piece of wood, $\frac{1}{2}$ in. thick and $6\frac{1}{2}$ ins. long by $3\frac{3}{4}$ ins. wide, will be required.

The lower corners should be cut away as in fig. 13. The base may be either polished or varnished. We also require a saddle of hard wood about $\frac{5}{16}$ in. thick on which to screw the magnet. A piece of wrought iron, $1\frac{3}{8}$ ins. long, $\frac{1}{2}$ in. wide, and $\frac{1}{8}$ in. thick, is now annealed in the same manner as the magnet core, and then filed up true and square for the armature, D. A piece of old clock-spring, $\frac{1}{4}$ in. wide, is now bent to form shown in fig. 13. The end, P, has two $\frac{1}{8}$-in. holes punched in, and the end, O, a small piece of platinum soldered on. The hammer, H, is made from a piece of $\frac{1}{16}$-in. iron wire, on one end of which is driven a piece of brass either in the form of a ball about $\frac{7}{16}$ in. in diameter, or shaped like the figure. The other end of the wire is firmly driven into the end of the armature. The clock-spring is now soldered on to the armature in the position shown. If the worker has the tools, a better job is to rivet the spring to the armature, as in fig. 13 at E.

Now take a brass wood screw, F, about 1 in. long, and file off the point. Drill a $\frac{1}{32}$-in. hole about $\frac{1}{8}$ in. deep in the end, and solder in a small piece of platinum wire. The end of the wire is now gently hammered over the end of the screw until it is about $\frac{1}{16}$ in. diameter. A small piece of thin springy brass, 1 in. long and $\frac{1}{4}$ in. wide, is bent like X in the figures, and drilled to just clear the screw just made.

We can now proceed to put the bell together. Commence by setting out the parts as shown in figs. 13, 14, and 15. The magnet is fixed in position by means of the large wood screw, as shown in fig. 15. The lower block of wood, and also the two smaller blocks which carry the armature and contact screw, are fixed in position by screws from the back of the baseboard. The armature is placed so that its centre line is the same height as the centres of the magnet ends, and $\frac{1}{8}$ in. clear of the ends.

Now place the contact screw block in position, and mark on the armature spring a point just opposite the platinum point of the screw. A small piece of platinum is soldered on the spring at this point. These pieces of platinum can be got at any electrical store for about 2d., or out of an old incandescent lamp. Get a broken or 'burnt-out' lamp and dig out the plaster in the cap. You will then find two scraps of a silver-like wire going through the glass. These are the platinum pieces required.

The gong, G, is better bought, and will cost about 3d. It is mounted on a short piece of brass tube, R, so that the hammer will strike it about $\frac{1}{8}$ in. above the rim, as in fig. 14. Two small hangers are let into the back of the baseboard, as shown in fig. 13, and a couple of terminals, T, screwed into the baseboard will complete the bell, except that it requires ' connecting up.'

This is done by taking the finishing end of the upper coil and coiling it round a piece of $\frac{1}{8}$-in. wire. Bare and clean about 1 in. of the end, and fasten it under the left-hand terminal. The finishing end of the lower coil is coiled and bared the same way, but the end is wrapped round the bend of the small brass, U, and soldered in place. A short piece of wire is now coiled round the $\frac{1}{8}$-in. wire, and both ends bared and cleaned. One end is fixed under the right hand terminal, and the other end is placed under the screw head which holds the armature spring to the wood block.

Our bell is now complete, except for a small wood box made from an old cigar box to cover in the works. The cover must have a slot cut in the under side to allow the hammer shaft to work.

Having made the bell, the beginner in electricity will enquire, " How is it that the bell will ring ? " When a current of electricity flows in a coil of wire placed round a piece of soft iron, the iron is converted into a magnet. When the current is cut off, the soft iron immediately loses its magnetism. If, therefore, a current is passed through the bell by connecting a battery to the terminals, we get a circuit through the coils, A and B (fig. 13), through the screw, F, the two pieces of platinum, spring E, and to the terminal. The current passing through the coils makes C C into a magnet, and attracts the armature, D. When D is attracted towards C C, the two platinum pieces no longer touch each other, and so the circuit is broken. The iron, C C, loses its magnetism, and spring, P E, brings the armature into its original position. This completes the circuit, and the cycle of operations is repeated. All this takes place very rapidly, and we get the well-known

C

sharp ring of the electric bell. The object of the platinum points is to prevent corrosion. When an electric current is switched on and off very rapidly, a great deal of sparking and burning takes place at the points of make and break, and platinum is about the only metal which will stand this treatment.

It is not generally known that an ordinary electric bell can be very easily transformed into a pretty effective shocking coil. The change is only temporary, not in the least affecting the material construction of the bell, and may be executed in a few minutes only. When a current is passing through the coils of the bell magnet, every time that the circuit is broken by the trembling action of the contact-breaker, an extra current—caused by self-induction—is produced, flowing in an opposite direction to that of the primary current from the battery. This extra, or secondary, current makes itself visible at the platinum contacts of the break as a short electric spark, since the E.M.F. is very high, usually amounting to several hundreds of volts. If two copper wires be attached to the circuit, one on each side of the contact-breaker, this current can be led off, and made more apparent to the nervous system, by grasping a couple of metallic· handles connected to the wires. The copper wires may be very thin—say No. 40 silk-covered, and should be made into flexible spirals by winding them round a wooden rod, such as a pencil. One wire is fastened to the brass screws which hold the armature-and-hammer spring in position, and the other to the brass pillar which carries the regulating screw for adjusting the speed of the break.

Before making the above connections, the ends of the wires must be scraped clean. The free ends of the wires may now be connected (preferably by soldering) to the handles, which may consist of two 3-in. lengths of $\frac{3}{4}$-in. brass tubing or rod, but a couple of zinc or tinplate cylinders will serve the purpose equally well. The battery should be a 1-pt. bichromate cell with lifting zinc, although a couple of quart Leclanchés will do fairly well. The strength of the shock is regulated by raising or lowering the zinc into the battery solution, or a water resistance may be employed.

Of course you cannot expect too much from such a makeshift, and, consequently, only one person at a time should try it, and usually it is almost unbearable. To obtain the maximum effect, the hands may be moistened with salt water.

As the ringing of the bell may prove undesirable, the gong may be screwed off for the time being, or, more simply, muffled with a piece of cloth. With a little ingenuity and a couple of metal finger rings, the novelty may be applied to an electric alarm, which is bound to waken the sleeper, who too often turns a deaf ear to the bell alone.

CHAPTER III

How to Make a Simple Telephone

THE following instructions will enable a handy reader to construct a practical telephone in a quite simple fashion, and which will be suitable either for work with a microphone or without. The latter method should be adopted for short distances only, and no battery will be required, but a second instrument similar to the first, and connected to it by 'line' wires, will be required instead.

It will be well to make a list of the under-mentioned articles, which will be needed for each instrument :—A piece of ferrotype plate, 3 ins. by 3 ins. ; about 1 drachm of No. 36 silk-covered copper wire ; 2 small brass terminals ; a 3-ins. by $\frac{1}{4}$-in. round bar magnet ; a piece of broom-handle $4\frac{1}{4}$ ins. long, and a tooth-powder box $1\frac{1}{4}$ ins. deep by $2\frac{1}{2}$ ins. diameter. Begin by drilling a full $\frac{1}{4}$-in. hole through the entire length of the piece of broom-handle This done, cut a hole in the bottom of box big enough to allow a tight fit on the wooden cylinder. Serve one end of the round wood with

hot glue, and push flush with the inside of the box.
Procure a piece of brass rod about $\frac{1}{8}$ in. thick,
and make a ring at one end 1 in. in diameter.
This will be found handy for hanging purposes.
Then cut a thread with screw-plate down to the
ring. Take a piece of sheet brass $\frac{1}{8}$ in. thick,
file a disc of the same diameter as one end of the
cylinder, as at B. In the centre of this drill and
tap an $\frac{1}{8}$-in. hole, so as to fit the brass rod. Two
other holes are made in this disc and countersunk
at opposite places on each side of the centre hole,

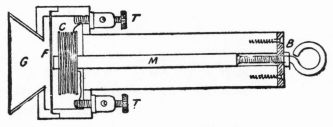

Fig. 16.—A Simple Telephone.

at equal distances apart. A small $\frac{1}{8}$-in. sheet-brass
nut is put on the rod.

The brass plate can now be screwed on the end
of the cylinder. If the magnet, M, has been bought
with a $\frac{1}{8}$-in. tapped hole at one end, the brass rod
may be screwed in; if not, it may be soldered
thereto. After this, make a cardboard bobbin 1 in.
long, with ends of the same diameter. Soak the
bobbin for a minute or two in melted paraffin wax,
and then wind carefully with about 1 drachm
36 silk-covered wire. Leave 3 ins. of wire out at

each end for connections with the terminals. Measure the exact inside diameter of the tooth-powder box, and cut a circle in stiff cardboard of the same size. Lay this on the ferrotype plate, and scratch lightly round with a sharp point. Take care not to make any dents on the plate, as this would be fatal to the working of the apparatus. Cut the disc out with a pair of scissors. A $1\frac{3}{4}$-in. hole must be cut in the centre of the box lid, and a cone of cardboard, G, glued in. All parts now being made, they can be put together. The magnet is slipped in the hole in the cylinder of wood, and the brass disc screwed to the top with a pair of small wood screws—if this has not already been done. The wound bobbin, C, is put on the magnet end, and the free ends of wire are soldered to two terminals, T T, as shown in the sketch. Place the ferrotype plate, F, in the mouth of the box lid, and put it on the box; then screw down the rod until, on tapping the ferrotype plate, the dull heavy sound indicates that the magnet is touching. Gently turn the rod in the opposite way, when the plate will give a clear sound. The telephone will now be ready for use.

CHAPTER IV

How to Make a Portable Shocking Coil

A SHOCKING COIL, such as that described below, can be made to afford a fund of amusement.

The first thing to make is the case (fig. 18), 10 ins. long, 4 ins. wide, and 4 ins. deep, and a lid to hinge over 2 ins. deep. The wood used is $\frac{1}{4}$-in. stuff, and given two coats of varnish stain. Now get a piece of wood, $9\frac{1}{2}$ ins. by $3\frac{1}{2}$ ins., for a base to mount coil on, and 2 ins. from right-hand end fix a piece of wood $1\frac{3}{4}$ ins. high, $1\frac{1}{2}$ ins. wide, $\frac{3}{8}$ in. thick, with $\frac{1}{2}$-in. hole to take the iron core covered with paper tube. The parts must be fixed perfectly rigid and square. The core is made from thin galvanised wire cut into 4-in. lengths, which have been left in the fire all night, and then packed tightly into the paper tube. Now wind the primary coil, which is started from the right-hand side, and wind on two layers of No. 20 B.W.G., silk-covered. This should be well served with shellac varnish.

The next operation is rather a tedious one—making the secondary coil, which slides bodily over

the primary.   Make a stout paper tube, just to fit
easily over the primary coil, 3 ins. long, and on each
end fasten by means of glue two wooden cheeks
$1\frac{3}{4}$ ins. high (bare) and 2 ins. wide.   When quite
dry and firm, well varnish, and wind on 2 ozs. of

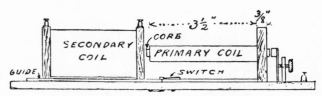

FIG. 17.—Arrangement of Shocking Coil.

No. 36 silk-covered copper wire, putting a sheet of
paraffin waxed paper between each coil.   Each end
of wire, when coil is wound, is to be fastened to a
terminal mounted on each cheek.   Now take the

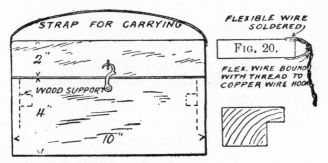

FIG. 18.—Box for carrying Shocking Coil.   FIG. 19.

baseboard, and fasten two strips of wood, $6\frac{1}{2}$ ins.
long (shaped as in fig. 19), $1\frac{1}{2}$ ins. apart (good), with
grooves inside, and on the bottom of each cheek of
secondary coil fasten a piece of brass about $\frac{1}{16}$ in.
thick, and long enough to project under the grooves

of the guides.   A contact-breaker must now be fitted in the usual manner, and have platinum contacts. A switch is next made under the base with three studs.   One stud is off; second stud current goes through a resistance of fine iron wire, such as that used by flower-sellers for tying up ' buttonholes '— 7 ins. will be sufficient ; and third stud current goes straight through the coil.   The switch arm is moved from a handle on top of baseboard.   Two pieces of wood are now put across the case to hold the coil about $\frac{1}{2}$ in. below the level of case when open.   A pair of handles (fig. 20) are made from 1-in. brass tube, about 4 ins. long, and fitted with $1\frac{1}{2}$ yards of flexible cord, which must be fixed very firmly to handles. Under the base is room for a dry battery, but a bichromate is recommended, as it lasts as long as three hours' continuous work, and a dry battery is not much good after half-an-hour.   A suitable bichromate battery should have two carbon plates ($5\frac{1}{2}$ ins. by $1\frac{3}{4}$ ins.) and one zinc (same size and well amalgamated).   It is a good plan to carry underneath a small tin of ground bichromate potash and small bottle of sulphuric acid, and a jar can be found wherever you go.   The general arrangement of the coil can be seen by fig. 17.   A useful addition is a scale on one of the bobbin guides, so as to compare different persons' strength.

CHAPTER V

How to Make a Simple Electric Motor

THIS little electric motor has the advantage that it can be constructed very cheaply, and, if properly made, will run at a great speed.

The magnet support (M S, fig. 21) and base are made from pieces of wood of suitable thicknesses, and varnished. The magnet, M, is made from a piece of soft iron rod, $\frac{1}{4}$ in. in diameter and about $4\frac{1}{2}$ ins. long. It is wound with No. 26 silk-covered wire, about 1 oz. The magnet is held down on the support by a piece of wood, W, laid across the magnet, and a screw passing through the wood, W, into the support.

The next things to make are the two bearings, B and B^1, of stout brass. One is straight, about $2\frac{1}{2}$ ins. long; the other shaped ⌐‾‾‾⌐ , about 1 in. long. In one end of each a conical hole is drilled for the spindle, S P, to run in. At the other ends two holes are drilled right through for the screws which fasten them to the base and magnet support.

The spindle is made from a fine knitting-needle, the ends filed to run in the conical holes in the bearings, B and B[1]. The armature is made of two square pieces of iron, I P, $\frac{3}{8}$ in. square, soldered to a piece of tin, T, about $1\frac{1}{2}$ ins. long. The armature must be soldered on the spindle, so that it runs quite true, as near the magnet as possible without

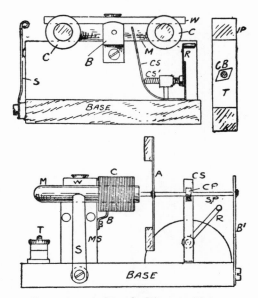

FIG. 21.—A Simple Electric Motor.

touching. The contact-breaker is a piece of copper, C B, shaped ⧄, about $\frac{3}{16}$ in. long, soldered on in a position as shown, but the best position is found by experiment. The spring, C S, is a piece of watch spring, which is made to approach or recede by the screw, C S[1], worked by the handle, R, which regulates the speed. A switch is fitted as shown at S.

Two terminals are fitted at the back. The current goes from terminal T to magnet, thence to bearing, through contact breaker and spring to switch, and from there to terminal, T^1, not shown.

The motor runs about 2000 revolutions per minute, with a quart bichromate, and is well worth making.

CHAPTER VI

HOW TO MAKE A PERMANENT MAGNET ELECTRO-MOTOR

THE motor here described, and illustrated in fig 22, gives a good insight into motor principles in general; it is very easy to construct, and runs well when carefully made. The field-magnet, F, first demands our attention. It consists of a permanent steel magnet with parallel limbs—4 ins. long, $\frac{1}{2}$ in. between limbs, metal $\frac{1}{2}$ in. wide and $\frac{1}{4}$ in. thick. This can be obtained from any electrical sundries dealer for about a shilling.

The armature, A, is made from a piece of soft iron about $4\frac{1}{2}$ ins. by $\frac{1}{2}$ in. by $\frac{1}{8}$ in. It is bent into horseshoe shape (the metal being heated to redness), with its limbs $1\frac{1}{2}$ ins. long and $\frac{7}{8}$ in. apart; it should be left to cool by itself. A central hole is drilled in this magnet, and a $3\frac{1}{2}$-in. spindle cut from a true and straight No. 19 steel knitting-needle. This is soldered firmly and truly in the armature, which should be well balanced. The spindle should protrude about $1\frac{1}{4}$ ins. on the commutator end, C.

Now a small collar of brass or copper is soldered on to the front end of the spindle, leaving about $\frac{3}{32}$ in. to enter the bearing.   This   bearing   is   the   front

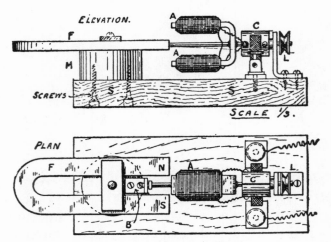

FIG. 22.—Permanent Magnetic Electric Motor.

bearing, B (fig. 23), and is made from a piece of brass $\frac{3}{4}$ in. by $\frac{3}{8}$ in. by $\frac{1}{16}$ in., $\frac{1}{4}$ in. of this being

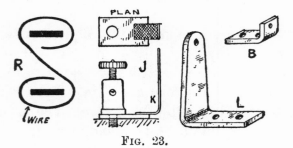

FIG. 23.

bent sharply at right angles.   (To bend brass and copper, the metal should be heated to a red heat and then quenched in water, after which it will bend well and without breaking.) In the longer end two small holes are drilled for the holding-down screws. The back bearing, L, is made from a piece of brass 2 ins. by $\frac{5}{8}$ in. by $\frac{1}{16}$ in. This is softened, and about $\frac{3}{4}$ in. is bent at right angles to the rest. The longest part may be tapered away towards the top, and neatly rounded. Two holes for holding-down screws are drilled in the short end.

The stand, S, is made of a piece of well-seasoned wood about 6 ins. by $2\frac{1}{2}$ ins. by $\frac{3}{4}$ in. This is well planed and sandpapered up, and then varnished or polished. The field-magnet saddle is then con-structed, and may be either round or square; a good size is $1\frac{1}{4}$ ins. square (or diameter) and $\frac{3}{4}$ in. high. The centre line of the stand is now care-fully obtained, and the saddle is screwed down near one end of the stand. A piece of brass, about $1\frac{1}{2}$ ins. by $\frac{1}{2}$ in. by $\frac{1}{8}$ in., is cut out, and a hole drilled in its centre. The field-magnet should now be screwed down on its saddle by means of this brass plate and a screw, which is driven into the centre of the saddle. Iron or steel must not be used for this holding-down piece, or it will much reduce the power of the magnet, owing to short-circuiting of the magnetic lines of force. A hole has now to be drilled in the front bearing, B, at such a height that when this is screwed on to the saddle, the field-magnet and spindle will be in the same plane. The front bear-ing is then screwed down, and the back bearing, L, put face to face with it, so that its hole may be marked off and drilled in the right place.

Now comes the most difficult part, namely, the commutator, C. It consists of a brass tube, $\frac{5}{8}$ in. diameter, and $\frac{5}{8}$ in. long, and about $\frac{1}{16}$ in. thick. This is forced on to a circular piece of ebonite or boxwood, in which a hole is drilled to fit the spindle. Four short brass screws are screwed into the tube and ebonite, two at each opposite end of a diameter, one of each of these being countersunk level with the surface of the tube, and filed smooth. Two saw cuts must be made at each end of a diameter, the diameter being at right angles to that of the screws. These saw cuts must be clean through the brass tube and a short way into the ebonite as well. The screws used to hold the two brass cheeks (just cut) on to the ebonite or boxwood must be short enough to quite clear the steel spindle. Such a commutator can be obtained for about 1s. 6d. from electrical dealers. It is troublesome to make, especially for those who do not possess a lathe, and it should run quite true when on the spindle. Now force the commutator on to the spindle so as to clear the armature by about $\frac{1}{8}$ in. Twist it so that its cuts are at the top and the bottom when the armature limbs are at the top and bottom. In other words, the saw cuts in the commutator must come under the brushes at the moment when the armature poles are directly opposite those of the field-magnets (see fig. 22).

The armature may now be mounted in its bearings. Place a small metal washer on the spindle between the commutator and the back bearing.

Slide the back bearing on the base until only a small amount of end play is allowed to the armature, and screw the back bearing down to the stand with two brass screws. Adjust the field-magnet to clear the armature by about $\frac{1}{32}$ in. to $\frac{1}{16}$ in. Take the armature and spindle out for winding.

The armature limbs must be covered with silk cloth or thin paper, so that not a bit of bare iron is left exposed. Commence winding by tying about 2 ins. of the wire (No. 26 D.C.C. or S.C.C. copper wire) to the commutator, and start winding along the limb, winding each wire close to its neighbour, and wind tight like a reel of cotton. When the end is getting near (say about half way), put a piece of silk, the same colour as the insulation of the wire, under the wire, and leave about an inch. Now wind on till you reach the end. Pull the silk up tight over the last wire, and wind back. Do this with every layer at each end. It prevents the under-layers slipping when the top ones are wound over them. Six layers must be got on each limb, making the total wire about 36 yards or 2 ozs. When crossing over to the second limb, wind the reverse way (see R, fig. 23) like an S. When both limbs are wound with the same number of layers (and turns as near as possible), the end of the winding must be firmly tied to the limb. Now cut off all the stray insulation which sticks to the unwound iron, and clean up. Test for leakage by cleaning one end of the winding and connecting any good cell to one end. Leave the other end of the

D

winding free. Touch a wire from the other pole of the cell on to a piece of the iron which has been scraped clean. If in a dark room no spark is seen when contact is made with the iron, there will be no leak. Connect the cell through the winding, and the armature should be a fairly powerful magnet. If it does not magnetise, there is a short circuit or a wire broken, and the armature must be re-wound. Clean both ends of winding and twist them under the two commutator screws; then drive the screws home.

All that remains to be done is to put some terminals and brushes on the machine. Cut two copper or brass blocks (see J, fig. 23) about $\frac{5}{8}$ in. by $\frac{7}{8}$ in. by $\frac{1}{16}$ in. or $\frac{1}{32}$ in. Drill a hole in each well towards one end to fit the tang of a binding screw. Cut two brushes of thin copper gauze about $1\frac{5}{8}$ in. by $\frac{3}{16}$ in., and solder them to these copper bits and bend them at right angles, K. Now place these blocks so that the brushes spring firmly on to the middle of the commutator; bore a hole for each binding screw, and screw them home. These brushes should only be one thickness of gauze, and should press firmly on to the commutator. The machine looks well with all the iron-work painted up one colour, and the coils shellaced, varnished red or black (mix red lead or lampblack with shellac varnish), and the saddle and base varnished or polished. The motor will run very fast with one Leclanché or any cell on, and at a furious speed with two cells on in series—even a piece of carbon and zinc in salt and water will make it work well.   The best cell for long runs is one made as follows: Porous pot with carbon and a solution of water, potassium-bichromate and sulphuric acid; outer cell, sheet zinc in salt and water.   The writer has run his little machine for fifty-four hours without a stop with one charge from the above cell, and at a speed somewhere near 2000 revolutions per minute.   A small metal or wooden pulley may be keyed on to the shaft at L.   The principle on which this motor acts is—" Similar magnetic poles repel; dissimilar poles attract."   The current is changed by the commutator always at such a time that the actions between the electro-magnet (armature) and permanent magnet (field) tend always to keep the former in motion.   This little machine is not self-starting, and, of course, very little work can be got out of it.

CHAPTER VII

HOW TO MAKE A SMALL ELECTRIC CAR MOTOR

MANY young readers find themselves unable, through not being the happy owners of a lathe, to build an electric car with the usual type of motor. An attempt is therefore made in this chapter to describe a motor of simple design which can be made with very few tools. It is shown fitted to a simple underframe on which can be built a car superstructure to suit the reader's individual taste. The requisite tools need include little besides a screwdriver, pocket knife, an old file, and bits of scrap metal to be found in any workshop.

The base, or carriage, is a piece of wood 6 ins. by 3 ins. by $\frac{3}{8}$ in. thick. A hole, $2\frac{1}{4}$ ins. by $1\frac{1}{2}$ ins., is cut $\frac{3}{4}$ in. from one side, and $1\frac{7}{8}$ ins. from one end of the base. Two pieces of iron rod are required, $\frac{3}{16}$ in. diameter, and bent to form and sizes of fig. 24.

Make four bobbins of stout paper to fit on these magnets, and wind them up until they are $\frac{1}{2}$ in. diameter with No. 28 single cotton-covered wire.

A round piece of wood, $1\frac{7}{8}$ ins. diameter and $1\frac{3}{8}$ ins. long, must now be mounted on a $2\frac{1}{4}$-ins. length of $\frac{1}{8}$-in. round steel wire $\frac{1}{2}$ inch from one end. Divide the circumference of the wooden drum into four equal parts, and let in four pieces of soft iron $1\frac{3}{8}$ ins. long by $\frac{1}{4}$ in. broad and $\frac{1}{8}$ in. thick. These must be let in level with the surface of the wood,

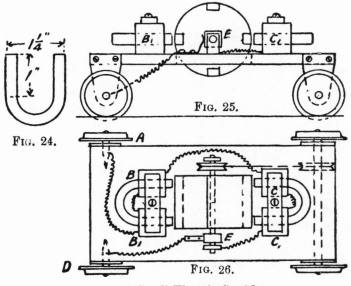

FIG. 24.

FIG. 25.

FIG. 26.

A Small Electric Car Motor.

and parallel to the spindle. In the model these figures are taken from, the soft iron armatures are held in place by a neat wrapping of small string $\frac{5}{8}$ in. broad, placed in the middle of the drum. A better way would be to drill and countersink a small hole at each end of each piece of iron, and fasten them down with small countersunk head screws. A small piece of brass, $\frac{1}{16}$ in. thick by $\frac{1}{2}$ in. square, must now be mounted on spindle in position shown in figs. 25 and 26 at E.

The drum must now be mounted in a pair of bearings made from strip brass. These bearings are fixed so that the drum can revolve in the hole made in the baseboard, and must be of such a height as to allow the two opposite iron armatures on the drum to be exactly opposite the ends of the electro-magnets, as in fig. 25. The electro-magnets are secured to the base by a piece of wood made to fit on the top of the coils, and a wood screw is passed through it between the coils and into the base. They are placed so that the drum, in revolving, just clears the ends of the magnets; hence it is important that the spindle should pass through the centre of the drum. A piece of spring brass, about $\frac{1}{64}$ in. thick or less, is bent at right angles and screwed to the base, so that it just touches the four corners of the square piece of brass on the spindle as it revolves.

The wheels may be mounted on axles running in short brackets screwed to the side of the base as is most convenient; only, remember that one wheel on each spindle must be disconnected either by an insulating bush or by being mounted separately. The latter way is perhaps the best and also the more simple method. Screw a piece of brass, about 1 in. wide at the top and $\frac{5}{16}$ in. at the bottom, to the base, the brass to be, say, $\frac{1}{8}$ in. thick. Then in the correct position screw on the wheel, a piece of wood behind the brass bracket acting as a 'nut' into which the screw may be driven. The screw should be large enough to allow the wheel to rotate without much shake, and should screw tightly into the wood behind the bracket and project through about $\frac{3}{16}$ in. The connections are as in figs. 25 and 26. From wheel, A, to starting end of coil, B_1; finish of coil, B_1, to finish of coil, B; start of coil B to start of coil C; finishing ends of coils, C and C_1, are connected together; the start of coil, C_1, to one drum-bearing, E, and contact breaker spring to wheel, D. The ends of the wires to the wheels are soldered to the screws which project through the brackets. The drum spindle may be connected to the wheels either by a cord or by gearing, as in larger electric cars.

The car is now finished, and should, if all connections are correct, work well with one bichromate cell. It should be said that, for the above connections to be correct, the coils must all be wound the same way round, and must be placed on the magnets with, say, all the starting ends towards the bends, and the finishing ends at the poles. This method will often save confusion, as when both ends are at the same end of the coil, the amateur worker is apt to forget which is the start, and which is the finish. It may also be stated that the car should run on metal rails through which the electric current is supplied. One pole of the battery is connected to each rail, and these must not be joined by metal 'sleepers.'

The sketches are not to scale, and just show the relative positions of the various parts.

CHAPTER VIII

How to Make a Simple Electric Beam Engine

THE little electric engine to be described, and an illustration of which is given in figs. 27 and 28, is one of the simplest electro-motors that can possibly be made; yet it has a good appearance if carefully constructed, and the particular one built by the writer runs at a great speed—certainly over a thousand revolutions a minute—when driven by two bichromate cells. It will, however, work well from one cell even of a Leclanché battery, and as this and an electro-magnet are the only 'expensive' items required, every reader will be able to build the machine, if he so desires.

We may commence with the electro-magnet, as being the mainspring of the whole motor. It will simplify matters to describe the engine already mentioned as having been built, and the dimensions for this particular case can readily be reduced or enlarged a little, more or less proportionately, to suit any other case, as required. It is as well to remember that the proportions given are by no means binding, and the intelligent amateur—though he be but a 'beginner'—will know pretty well where they may be modified to suit his own needs.

The electro-magnet, then, as used in the engine illustrated, is of the ordinary electric bell pattern, with iron pole pieces $\frac{3}{8}$ in. diameter by $1\frac{3}{4}$ ins. long, and a yoke $\frac{7}{8}$ in. wide, $\frac{1}{4}$ in. thick, and $2\frac{1}{4}$ ins.

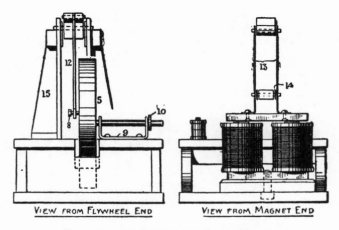

VIEW FROM FLYWHEEL END   VIEW FROM MAGNET END

FIG. 27.—Model Electric Beam Engine.

long. Each pole has a neat wood bobbin fitting on it, which is filled with No. 26 wire to an outside diameter of $1\frac{1}{8}$ ins. The amateur who has a dismantled electric bell in fair condition is already provided with a suitable electro-magnet. A second-hand one may be readily bought, or one can be forged from round or flat iron, which must be *soft*. As numerous ways of making the magnet can be found, there is no need to particularise very minutely. The magnet should have the poles filed level, and wound (on the poles only), to a out three times the diameter of the iron, with

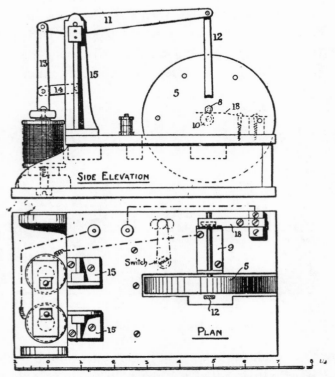

FIG. 28.—General Arrangement of Model Electric Beam Engine.

some fine wire, Nos. 24, 26, or 28 being suitable, the last two especially.

So many amateurs feel doubtful as to the right way to wind an electro-magnet of this kind, that I must be pardoned if an undue space be taken up to show how it should be done. Everyone knows

how to wind a straight (bar) magnet, shown dia-
grammatically at fig. 29A. Fig. 29B is the same,
but shows two layers of wire, the second being
continued back over the first. Now, fig. 30 is
simply a bar magnet wound as in fig. 29A, and
bent into a horseshoe form. Follow the winding
of fig. 30, and you will see it is precisely as in
fig. 29A. But horseshoe magnets are usually not
horseshoe at all—if the Irishism be allowed—but
have straight poles and a straight yoke. It is in-
convenient to wind the yoke, and there is practically

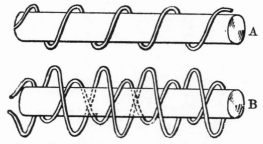

Fig. 29.—Winding a Straight Bar Magnet.

no need to do it. Suppose the points *a* and *b* in
fig. 30 be joined by a wire (as shown dotted); all
the wire at *c, d, e* may now be eliminated—not, it
is true, without any loss in magnetic effect, but
with a decided gain from a practical point of view.
Now, if the round part of the magnet be exchanged
for a straight yoke, the winding being the same, we
step at once to the ordinary bell magnet, winding as
shown in fig. 31, which is obviously the same in
essentials as figs. 30 and 29. That should make
the principle quite clear.

The electro-magnet being disposed of, we may proceed to construct the flywheel and crank. The former consists of a good-sized coffee-tin lid, about 4 ins. diameter and $\frac{1}{2}$ in. wide, a plain lid being preferable for the purpose. First find the actual diameter of the lid *inside*, and then with a pair of compasses describe a circle, this size exactly, on a piece of nicely planed wood a little less than $\frac{1}{2}$ in. thick. Cut this out carefully with a fretsaw to

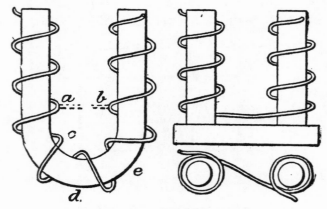

FIGS. 30 and 31.—Horseshoe Magnets.

get an accurately circular disc. Find a large French nail; one about 3 ins. long and $\frac{3}{16}$ in. diameter will be right. At the centre of the wood disc (marked by the compass leg) drill a small hole as carefully as possible to get it exactly at right angles. Try if it is correct by means of a straight wire fitting the hole, and a set square or ordinary steel square. If correct, drill the hole larger, being careful to follow the first hole, and make it big enough to allow the French nail to be driven in tight.

Before putting in the nail, about $\frac{1}{2}$ in. of its point end should be cut off square.   The hole in the wood disc on one side must then be counter-

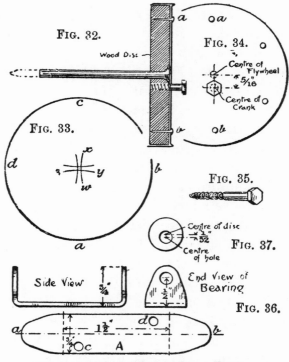

Details of Model Electric Beam Engine.

sunk a little to allow the head of the nail to go in almost flush. I say 'almost,' because it will be better, if anything, for the head to stand out a trifle. Drive the nail in—it should go in quite tight, and then put the tin lid over the disc, which should, of

course, fit inside it fairly tightly.   Reference to fig.
32 will help to make matters clear.

In fig. 32 may also be seen at $a\,b$ two little
tacks.   There should be half-a-dozen of these disposed equally round the wheel, and they may be
driven straight through the tin into the disc of
wood, if the latter be supported on something solid
just underneath.   Round-headed brass tacks, of
course, look best, but are not indispensable.

If everything has been carefully done, the wheel
should run pretty truly with the nail as axle, but
if carelessly or unluckily mounted, it may ' wobble '
or run eccentrically.   In the first case, the remedy
is to knock the nail square with the disc, and fix it
there with a piece of brass plate, or even wood,
screwed to the disc and bearing hard on the nail on
the side towards which it tends to incline.   In the
other case, if the eccentricity is little, it must be
put up with.   If much, a new wood disc, more
carefully cut out, is the only remedy.

The next thing is to find the centre of the flywheel.   This can be done by means of a pair of
calipers.   They should be opened as near as can be
guessed to the half-diameter, one leg placed at a
(fig. 33), and the arc, $z\,y$, struck on the tin.   Then
one leg is placed at b, and the arc, $w\,x$, is marked.
This is done again at c and b, when the centre of
the wheel is quite apparent.   At a distance of
$\frac{5}{16}$ in. from the centre (see fig. 34) make a mark
and drill a hole suitable to take a No. 6 wood
screw.   This hole can be punched and rimmered out

with a tang end of a file. Prepare a round-headed No. 6 brass or iron screw by filing the round head down to a disc, and filing this again to a hexagon (fig. 35); *this* is not an essential, but it adds to appearance, costs but little time, and is good practice. This screw has to be driven nice and square into the hole in flywheel; it should project about $\frac{1}{4}$ in., and forms the crank pin of the engine.

The bearings may be made in one stiff piece of brass 3 ins. long, $\frac{3}{4}$ in. wide, and $\frac{1}{16}$ in. to $\frac{1}{8}$ in. thick. This should be filed to the shape shown at A (fig. 36), and the two ends bent up at the dotted lines, so that each end is $\frac{3}{4}$ in. high, and the middle piece $1\frac{1}{2}$ ins. long. If a centre line, $a\,b$, has been marked on what will be the outside of the bearing, it will be an advantage in setting out the holes for the shaft. These holes must both be marked off at the same height, and drilled to suit the shaft. The beginner will doubtless drill the largest hole he can to start with, and rimmer it out with the tang end of the file. The motor built for the purposes of this article is as innocent of lathe work as any 'machinery,' and the drilling was no exception— yet it runs, and runs well.

The holes in bearings must be no bigger than will allow the shaft to run in them quite easily; they must, of course, be in line. Drill two holes in the base part of the bearing $c\,d$ (fig. 36) close to the edge, and big enough to take any ordinary screw—say, $\frac{3}{4}$ in. long.

Before quitting this part of the machine, the

contact piece on shaft may be described. It may be a circular piece of brass, filed to shape, and about $\frac{3}{8}$ in. diameter. It has a hole drilled so that it will just *drive* on the shaft (by which is meant the French nail); but the centre of this hole is about $\frac{1}{32}$ in. away from the real centre of the disc. It can all be seen in fig. 37, by which it will be observed that the contact piece is really a little eccentric. A farthing is rather larger, but might form a handy ready-made disc.

The oscillating beam for the engine looks like

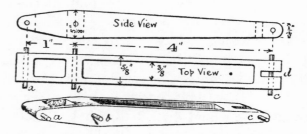

FIG. 38.—Wooden Beam for Electric Beam Engine.

a massive casting, but this it is not. It is simply a piece of wood cut to the shape shown in fig. 38. The spaces seen in the top view are cut out with fretsaw, simply to lighten and add to the appearance of the beam, and holes are drilled at *a, b, c* very accurately, to take three $1\frac{1}{2}$-in. French nails tightly. A space is cut out at *d* for the connecting-rod top end.

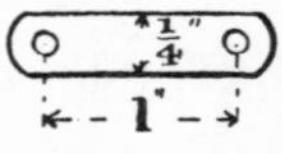

The connecting-rod is a piece of stoutish brass—say $\frac{1}{16}$ in. thick—shaped as in fig. 39. Many of the parts, such as this connecting-rod, can be made

FIG. 42.

quite as readily from a sketch, as given, as from many lines of description. The hole at top end must be big enough to run freely—but not too slack—on the French nail at *c* in fig. 38, and the other hole must similarly fit the neck of the screw crank-pin (fig. 35). Filing is the method adapted to make the rod.

The armature for the electro-magnet is the next

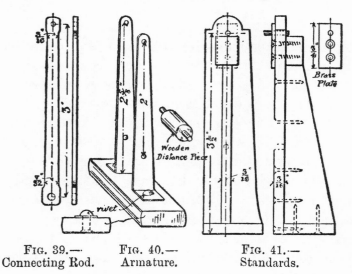

FIG. 39.—   FIG. 40.—   FIG. 41.—
Connecting Rod.   Armature.   Standards.

item. The more substantial it is the better, and in my case it is about 2 ins. long, $\frac{3}{4}$ in. wide, and full $\frac{1}{4}$ in. thick. Any odd piece of soft iron is suitable, as, for example, a portion of a broken wall bracket, which does service in the present engine. The armature is carried by two thin pieces of brass (fig. 40) which are fixed by rivets. These latter consist of portions of round-headed

E

iron screws, riveted with countersunk holes on the underside of the armature, as shown in the little section of same. The riveting must be well done, as there is some considerable strain. The sizes of the brass suspending-pieces are given, and all the holes shown are just big enough to run easily on the $1\frac{1}{2}$-in. French nails already mentioned.

A pair of links of thin brass like fig. 42 are also required, and holes to run easily on the small French nails.

The upright supports for the beam require to be nicely made. Thin fretwood or cigar-box wood is suitable, and the construction is shown in several views in fig. 41, in which is shown a brass plate with three holes. The top one carries the French nail shaft, b, in fig. 38, whilst the other two are countersunk for screws which go through the upright and into a neat wood block. The base is fitted exactly at right angles to the upright pieces with glue and stout pins, while a web is fitted and fixed by glue and pins to the structure. A hole is drilled to take a $1\frac{1}{2}$-in. French nail tightly at d. Two standards as described are needed, and must be identical.

All is now ready for building up. A baseboard of any smooth flat wood, 8 ins. long, $4\frac{1}{2}$ ins. wide, and not under $\frac{3}{8}$ in. thick, is to be made, and also an 'upper floor,' $6\frac{1}{4}$ ins. by $4\frac{1}{2}$ ins. by $\frac{3}{8}$ in. These are made into the form sketched in fig. 43 by two sides, S S, of stout wood, but, before fixing together, a slot, as shown, must be cut out of the top floor for the flywheel, and strengthening pieces, as given in the drawing (figs. 27 and 28), must be affixed under-neath. These need not be nicely finished off, but must be stout enough to take screws without splitting. They are secured to top, bottom, and sides of box by means of screws.

Referring to figs. 27 and 28, take the fly-wheel, 5 (to the crank pin of which the connecting rod, 12, has been attached), and thread the shaft through one of the journal holes in the bearing. Now drive the eccentric contact disc on the shaft to about $\frac{1}{2}$ in. from the outward end. The eccentric must have a definite position with regard to the crank, the longest side of the eccentric being at right angles to the crank itself. This position is shown at 10 in fig. 28, and is such that when the crank is at its lowest point, and the armature at its highest, the eccentric just begins to make contact with a spring, 18, and continues in contact until the crank has reached its highest and the armature its lowest point. Thread the shaft through the second bearing, which must come close up to the eccentric. Put the flywheel in its place in the slot, F (fig. 43), so that it has an equal space on each side of it, and screw down the bearing, 9, with two round-headed screws.

The beam (fig. 38) may be laid on the bedplate, and its position marked off. It will then be easy to see where the standards (15, in figs. 27 and 28) are to be put to support it, and also where to fix the electro-magnet. The French nails are fitted in their respective places, joining up the connecting

rod, armature, standards, and beam, and also joining
the short links, 14, to standards and armature.

A contact-spring of very thin springy brass oi
copper, as shown in No. 18 (fig. 28), is fitted in the
position shown in the general view.   It has one
hole near the end, by which it is fastened to the
wood block, a copper wire being looped under the
spring here.   Another hole a little further along
takes a screw, which passes into the base, and this
screw is used to regulate the pressure.   As already

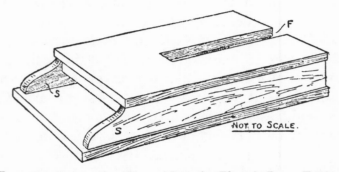

FIG. 43.—Perspective View of Base for Electric Beam Engine.

hinted, the position of the contact-spring should be
such that contact is made during half a revolution
of the flywheel.   The wire from contact-screw goes
direct to one of the terminals on the baseboard.
Another wire, attached to one of the screws of the
bearing, 9, is led to one end of the electro-magnet
winding, the other end of which goes direct to the
second terminal.

If it is desired, one of these wires can be broken,
and a simple switch inserted, as shown in dotted

lines in the plan view (fig. 28). A more ambitious arrangement could easily be devised by making the switch of an upright lever type, like the reversing lever of a locomotive engine.

Except for painting up, which can be done to the taste of the amateur, the model is now finished, and will run at great speed if the wires from either of the batteries previously mentioned be attached to the terminals. A tiny drop of oil on each of the bearings will greatly improve the running, and does not appear to interfere with the flow of the current through the shaft and bearings. Too much pressure on the contact-spring is not advisable, nor too little; but this can be regulated by means of the screw provided for the purpose.

It is worth noting that the whole of the work must be *strong*. The pull of the electro-magnet is so powerful that it will soon knock the machine to pieces if not well fitted on a strong, rigid base. The electro-magnet must be so fixed that the armature, when at its lowest position, just clears the poles by $\frac{1}{32}$ in., and contact should cease just before the armature reaches that point, or the motor will make a terrible noise, which, while it is music to the enthusiastic builder, is perfectly distracting to friends and neighbours! Finally, though it is perhaps unnecessary, it may yet be worth while stating that the horse-power of this little machine is *not* to be measured in integers—nay, it may best be expressed in decimals—but it *will* run, and that is one good quality in a working model!

PRINTED BY NEILL AND CO., LTD., EDINBURGH.